# Maus I: My Father Bleeds History

Art Spiegelman

## STUDENT PACKET

**NOTE:**

The trade book edition of the novel used to prepare this guide is found in the Novel Units catalog and on the Novel Units website. Using other editions may have varied page references.

Please note: We have assigned Interest Levels based on our knowledge of the themes and ideas of the books included in the Novel Units sets, however, please assess the appropriateness of this novel or trade book for the age level and maturity of your students prior to reading with them. You know your students best!

**ISBN 978-1-60878-123-2**

To order, contact your
local school supply store, or:

Toll-Free Fax: 877.716.7272
Phone: 888.650.4224
3901 Union Blvd., Suite 155
St. Louis, MO 63115

sales@novelunits.com

novelunits.com

# Note to the Teacher

Selected activities, quizzes, and test questions in this Novel Units® Student Packet are labeled with the following reading/language arts skills for quick reference. These skills can be found above quiz/test questions or sections and in the activity headings.

**Basic Understanding:** The student will demonstrate a basic understanding of written texts. The student will:
- use a text's structure or other sources to locate and recall information (Locate Information)
- determine main idea and identify relevant facts and details (Main Idea and Details)
- use prior knowledge and experience to comprehend and bring meaning to a text (Prior Knowledge)
- summarize major ideas in a text (Summarize Major Ideas)

**Literary Elements:** The student will apply knowledge of literary elements to understand written texts. The student will:
- analyze characters from a story (Character Analysis)
- analyze conflict and problem resolution (Conflict/Resolution)
- recognize and interpret literary devices (flashback, foreshadowing, symbolism, simile, metaphor, etc.) (Literary Devices)
- consider characters' points of view (Point of View)
- recognize and analyze a story's setting (Setting)
- understand and explain themes in a text (Theme)

**Analyze Written Texts:** The student will use a variety of strategies to analyze written texts. The student will:
- identify the author's purpose (Author's Purpose)
- identify cause and effect relationships in a text (Cause/Effect)
- identify characteristics representative of a given genre (Genre)
- interpret information given in a text (Interpret Text)
- make and verify predictions with information from a text (Predictions)
- sequence events in chronological order (Sequencing)
- identify and use multiple text formats (Text Format)
- follow written directions and write directions for others to follow (Follow/Write Directions)

**Critical Thinking:** The student will apply critical-thinking skills to analyze written texts. The student will:
- write and complete analogies (Analogies)
- find similarities and differences throughout a text (Compare/Contrast)
- draw conclusions from information given (Drawing Conclusions)
- make and explain inferences (Inferences)
- respond to texts by making connections and observations (Making Connections)
- recognize and identify the mood of a text (Mood)
- recognize an author's style and how it affects a text (Style)
- support responses by referring to relevant aspects of a text (Support Responses)
- recognize and identify the author's tone (Tone)
- write to entertain, such as through humorous poetry or short stories (Write to Entertain)
- write to express ideas (Write to Express)
- write to inform (Write to Inform)
- write to persuade (Write to Persuade)
- demonstrate understanding by creating visual images based on text descriptions (Visualizing)
- practice math skills as they relate to a text (Math Skills)

Name _____

## Getting the "Lay of the Land"

**Directions:** Prepare for reading by answering the following short-answer questions.

1. Who is the author?

   _____

2. What does the title suggest to you about the book?

   _____

   _____

   _____

   _____

3. When was the book first copyrighted?

   _____

4. How many pages are there in the book?

   _____

5. Thumb through the book. Read three pages—one from near the beginning, one from near the middle, and one from near the end. What predictions can you make about the book?

   _____

   _____

   _____

   _____

   _____

6. What does the cover suggest to you about the book?

   _____

   _____

   _____

   _____

Name _____

## Anticipation and Reaction

**Directions:** Consider the following statements before you read the book. Place a checkmark in one of the boxes to show whether you agree or disagree with each statement, and provide your reasoning. After you have completed the book, mark your response again. Provide an explanation if your opinion has changed.

| Statement | Response Before Reading | Response After Reading |
|---|---|---|
| 1. In the face of death, people will betray each other and think only of themselves. | ☐ you agree with the statement <br> ☐ you disagree with the statement | ☐ you agree with the statement <br> ☐ you disagree with the statement |
| 2. Fathers and sons often share many traits, and this can cause problems. | ☐ you agree with the statement <br> ☐ you disagree with the statement | ☐ you agree with the statement <br> ☐ you disagree with the statement |
| 3. Tragedies that occur during youth drastically affect a person's habits and beliefs later in life. | ☐ you agree with the statement <br> ☐ you disagree with the statement | ☐ you agree with the statement <br> ☐ you disagree with the statement |

© Novel Units, Inc.

Name _____

## Vocabulary Multiple Choice & Summary

| | | | |
|---|---|---|---|
| regards | textiles | sheik | engaged |
| dowry | hosiery | gefilte | Holocaust |

**Directions:** Choose the word closest in meaning to the vocabulary word as it is used in the book. Then use at least five of the words in a brief summary of Vladek's youth.

_____ 1. **regards:**    (a) rants      (b) rationales      (c) reports      (d) respects

_____ 2. **textiles:**    (a) machines      (b) materials      (c) memories      (d) monologues

_____ 3. **Holocaust:** (a) gambit      (b) generation      (c) genocide      (d) government

_____ 4. **sheik:**    (a) layman      (b) leader      (c) ledger      (d) lobbyist

_____ 5. **gefilte:**    (a) charred      (b) cheap      (c) chopped      (d) chunky

_____ 6. **engaged:**    (a) betrayed      (b) betrothed      (c) blinded      (d) bothered

_____ 7. **hosiery:**    (a) skirts      (b) slippers      (c) spectacles      (d) stockings

_____ 8. **dowry:**    (a) pain      (b) payment      (c) pride      (d) promise

_____

_____

_____

_____

_____

_____

_____

_____

_____

_____

_____

## Word Map

| prevention | Communist | seamstress | sanitarium |
|---|---|---|---|
| pogrom | synagogues | hemorrhaging | |

**Directions:** Complete a word map like the one below for each vocabulary word above.
(Note: If there is no antonym for the word, you may write "not applicable.")

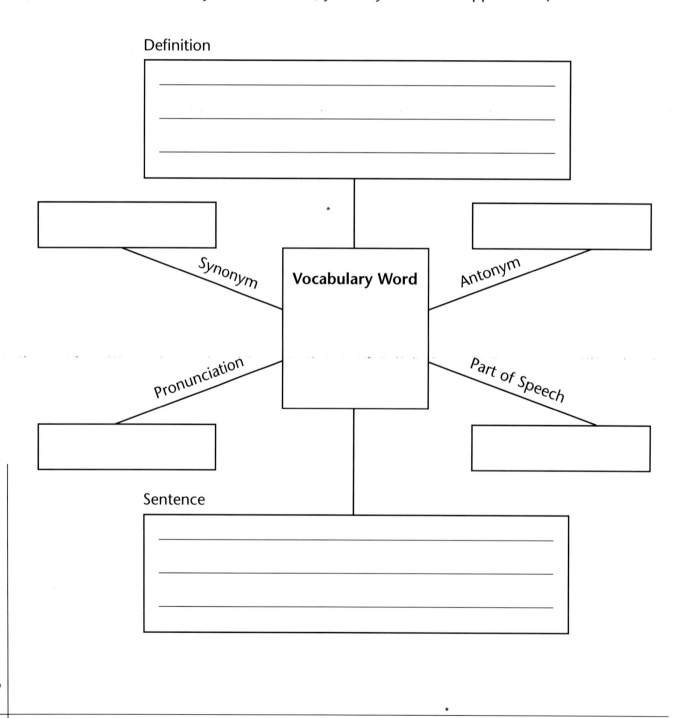

Definition

Synonym

**Vocabulary Word**

Antonym

Pronunciation

Part of Speech

Sentence

## Vocabulary/Plot Association

| | | | |
|---|---|---|---|
| assignments | abundant | Torah | rabbi |
| Gestapo | systematic | protectorate | recuperating |

**Directions:** Select four of the above vocabulary words, and on the lines below, explain in two to three sentences why each word is important to the plot of *Maus I.*

Word #1: _____

_____

_____

_____

Word #2: _____

_____

_____

_____

Word #3: _____

_____

_____

_____

Word #4: _____

_____

_____

_____

Name _____

## Vocabulary by Association

| luxurious | chronological | vacated | proposition |
|---|---|---|---|
| convalescent | deported | vaguely | |

**Directions:** Define and associate each vocabulary word above with a character from *Maus I*, and in the chart below, explain why that word matches your chosen character's personality. You may associate more than one word with a character, but use no more than three words per character.

| Word(s) | Character | Explanation |
|---|---|---|
| | | |
| | | |
| | | |
| | | |
| | | |
| | | |
| | | |

## Vocabulary Crossword Puzzle

| | | | |
|---|---|---|---|
| meshugah | neurotic | obscure | objective |
| liquidate | commission | seizure | estate |

**Directions:** Using the vocabulary words above, create a crossword puzzle answer key by filling in the grid below. Be sure to number the squares for each word. Blacken any spaces not used by the letters. Then, write clues to the crossword puzzle. Number the clues to match the numbers in the squares. The teacher will give each student a blank grid. Make a blank copy of your crossword puzzle for other students to answer. Exchange your clues with someone else, and solve the blank puzzle s/he gives you. Check the completed puzzles with the answer keys.

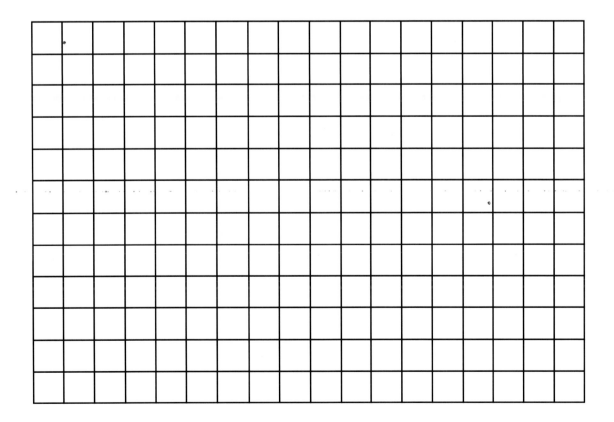

## Vocabulary Synonyms & Antonyms

| pragmatic | caricature | senile | outskirts |
|---|---|---|---|
| acquaintances | Yiddish | | |

**Directions:** Each sentence below contains an antonym or a synonym of a vocabulary word in the box above. Write the correct related vocabulary word in the provided space, and circle all antonyms.

1. The naïve student believed that his teacher would accept his outlandish excuse for

   showing up without homework. _____

2. The newspaper fired the artist for drawing a very offensive stereotype of the President.

   _____

3. Jack did not understand the European exchange student because the student only spoke

   a German-inspired language. _____

4. When the troops reached the center of town, they realized the enemy was long gone.

   _____

5. Michelle was worried because her old dog Wrinkle had become terribly forgetful.

   _____

6. Lisa made many business connections in college, and she hoped they might help her

   start her own business. _____

**Directions:** On a separate sheet of paper, write a brief answer to each question as you read the book at home or in class. Use the questions to guide your reading, prepare for class discussions, and review for quizzes and tests.

## The Sheik

1. Where does Art's father live?
2. Why does Vladek criticize Mala when Art arrives?
3. Who was Lucia, and how did Vladek feel about her?
4. Why did Vladek choose Anja over Lucia?
5. Why didn't Anja's parents want her to visit Vladek? What did Vladek do instead?
6. What kind of family did Anja come from?
7. What did Vladek find in Anja's closet? What did he discover about this item?
8. Why did Anja ignore Vladek for a period of time? Who was to blame for this?
9. Why does Vladek want Art to keep Anja and Lucia out of his story?

## The Honeymoon

1. What kinds of pills does Vladek take? According to Vladek, why must he take them?
2. How did Anja initially get into trouble with the law? What did she do to escape this trouble?
3. What kind of business did Vladek wish to open? What did Anja's father suggest Vladek do instead?
4. What causes Vladek to spill his pills, and how does he react?
5. Why did Anja's family call Vladek in Bielsko? Where did Anja go after this?
6. What did Anja and Vladek see that frightened them? What stories had they heard about the Nazis at this point?
7. How did Vladek help Anja recover?
8. What happened to Vladek's factory while he was at the sanitarium with Anja?
9. What did Vladek receive in the mail from the Polish government? How did this affect his family?

## Prisoner of War

1.  What childhood memory does Art reveal to Mala at the dinner table before Vladek continues his tale?

2.  How did Vladek's father try to save himself and his children from having to join the army?

3.  Why did the Polish officer scold Vladek? Why did the Nazi soldiers become angry with Vladek after they captured him?

4.  What task did the Nazis assign Vladek to help with at the prison camp, and why was the task impossible?

5.  How did Vladek attempt to stay healthy and mentally acute while in the prison camp?

6.  What opportunity did the Nazis offer the prisoners, and why did Vladek take advantage of this opportunity?

7.  What premonition did Vladek have, and from whom?

8.  Who was Orbach, and how did he help Vladek?

9.  How did Vladek's father lose his beard?

10. What happens to Art's jacket? How does Art respond to his father's gift?

## The Noose Tightens

1.  What does Vladek wish to fix, and how does Art respond?

2.  After Vladek went to live with the Zylberbergs in 1940, how did he make money?

3.  Why did the Nazis close down the entire street one day? How did Vladek avoid them, and what did he do to ensure his safety in the future?

4.  What items did the Nazis want from the Zylberbergs, and how did they finally get them?

5.  Why did the Nazis hang Nahum Cohn?

6.  What new orders did the Nazis issue regarding the elderly? How did the Zylberbergs initially respond, and why did they finally give in?

7.  Why were Jews instructed to gather at *Dienst* Stadium? Why did Vladek's father sneak to the other side of the fence?

8.  Of what does Mala accuse Vladek? How does Art respond?

 © Novel Units, Inc.

## Mouse Holes

1. Why does Mala call Art early in the morning, and how does Art react?

2. About what is Vladek upset the next time Art comes to visit? Why is Vladek embarrassed?

3. Describe the last time Art saw his mother.

4. What did Persis offer Vladek's family? How did Vladek's family react, and what eventually happens to Richieu?

5. Where were Vladek's family's two bunkers in Srodula? Why did the family build them?

6. How did the Nazis find the family's second bunker?

7. Who was Haskel, and why couldn't he help Anja's parents?

8. What kinds of items does Vladek collect? What does Art think about this habit?

9. Who was Miloch, and what did he show Vladek?

10. What does Vladek tell Art about Mala? How does Vladek feel about his second marriage?

## Mouse Trap

1. What worries Art about the book he is writing?

2. How does Vladek feel about Art's preliminary sketches of the book? To what cartoonist does Vladek compare Art?

3. How did Richieu's governess react when Anja and Vladek sought her help? How did Mr. Lukowski help the couple?

4. Who was Mrs. Motonowa, and how did she help Anja and Vladek? Why did they have to avoid her husband?

5. What deal did smugglers offer Vladek and other Jews? How did Vladek and the others verify that the smuggling plan would work?

6. What did Anja think of the smuggling plan? How were she and Vladek caught?

7. How was Vladek able to acquire food for Anja while they were in prison?

8. Why does Art call his father a "murderer"?

## Feelings

**Directions:** Complete the chart below to analyze Vladek's feelings in *Maus I*.

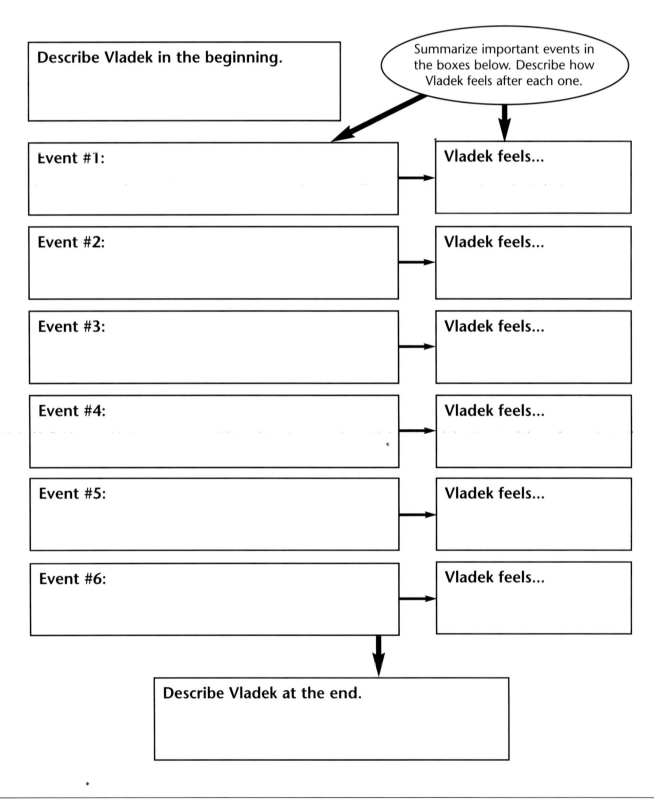

| Describe Vladek in the beginning. | Summarize important events in the boxes below. Describe how Vladek feels after each one. |

Event #1: → Vladek feels...

Event #2: → Vladek feels...

Event #3: → Vladek feels...

Event #4: → Vladek feels...

Event #5: → Vladek feels...

Event #6: → Vladek feels...

Describe Vladek at the end.

## Sociogram

**Directions:** On the "spokes" surrounding each character's name, write several adjectives that describe that character. How does one character influence another? On the arrows joining one character to another, write a description of the relationship between the two characters. Remember, relationships go both ways, so each line requires a descriptive word.

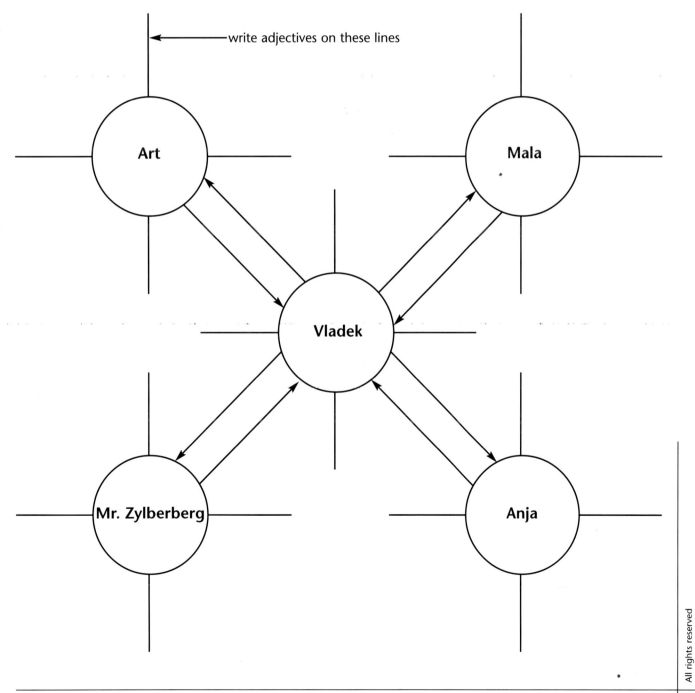

Name _____

## Bio-poem

**Directions:** Using the format below, write a bio-poem about Art or Vladek. Then write a bio-poem about yourself using the same format. Write a paragraph describing the values and characteristics you share.

—Line  1: First name only
—Line  2: Lover of (list three things character loves)
—Line  3: Giver of (list three things character gives)
—Line  4: Needs (list three things character needs)
—Line  5: Wants (list three things character wants)
—Line  6: Is good at (list three things character is good at)
—Line  7: Should work on (list three things character needs to improve)
—Line  8: Is similar to (list three people or other characters to whom this character is similar and list a reason behind each character)
—Line  9: Survivor of (list three things the character survives)
—Line 10: Last name only

Title _____

1. _____
2. _____
3. _____
4. _____
5. _____
6. _____
7. _____
8. _____
9. _____
10. _____

Name _____

## Solving Problems

**Directions:** List six problems the characters in the book face. Then complete the rest of the chart. For each problem, circle which solution you think is best—yours or the character's.

| Problem | Character's Solution | Your Solution |
|---------|----------------------|---------------|
|         |                      |               |
|         |                      |               |
|         |                      |               |
|         |                      |               |
|         |                      |               |
|         |                      |               |

## Similes and Metaphors

**A. Directions:** Read the quotes from the book below. Each uses a simile or metaphor to compare two things. In the blank boxes next to each quote, write what the simile or metaphor really means.

| Quote | Rewrite |
|---|---|
| 1. "Last one to the schoolyard is a rotten egg" (p. 5)! | |
| 2. "Doctors, they only give me 'junk food'..." (p. 26). | |
| 3. "You both [Art and Mala] think money grows on bushes" (p. 73). | |

**B. Directions:** Now, read the quotes from the book. The quotes given DO NOT use similes or metaphors. This time, rewrite each quote so that it DOES use a simile or metaphor.

| Quote | Rewrite |
|---|---|
| 4. "This the Germans did very good... always they did everything very systematic" (p. 59). | |
| 5. "That coffee's completely stale" (p. 68)! | |

Name _____

## Using Dialogue

**Directions:** Choose some dialogue from the book. Fill in the chart to evaluate the purpose of the dialogue and whether or not it is effective in moving along the plot.

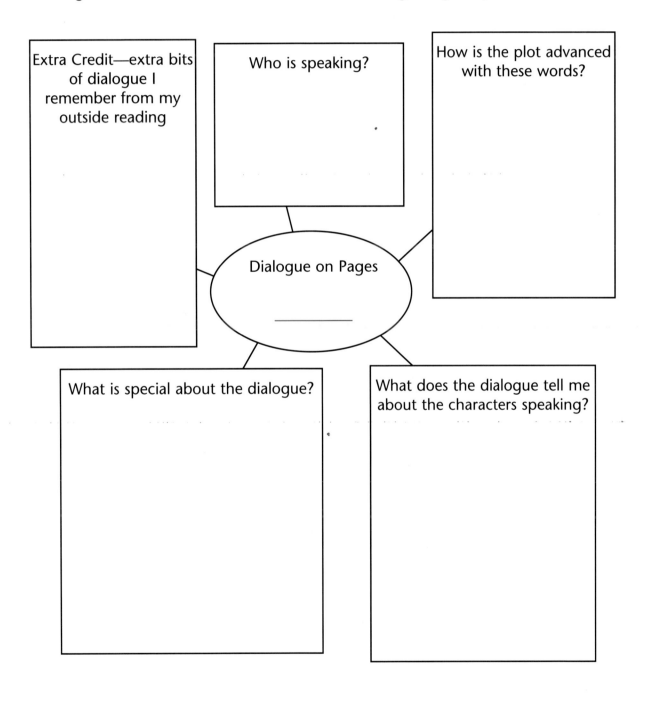

Extra Credit—extra bits of dialogue I remember from my outside reading

Who is speaking?

How is the plot advanced with these words?

Dialogue on Pages
_____

What is special about the dialogue?

What does the dialogue tell me about the characters speaking?

## Pros and Cons

**Directions:** On the lines below, describe the pros and cons of Vladek burning Anja's journals.

**Vladek burned Anja's journals.**

Pros

Cons

_____

_____

_____

_____

_____

_____

_____

_____

_____

_____

_____

_____

_____

_____

Name _____

## Story Map

**Directions:** Fill in each box below with information about the book.

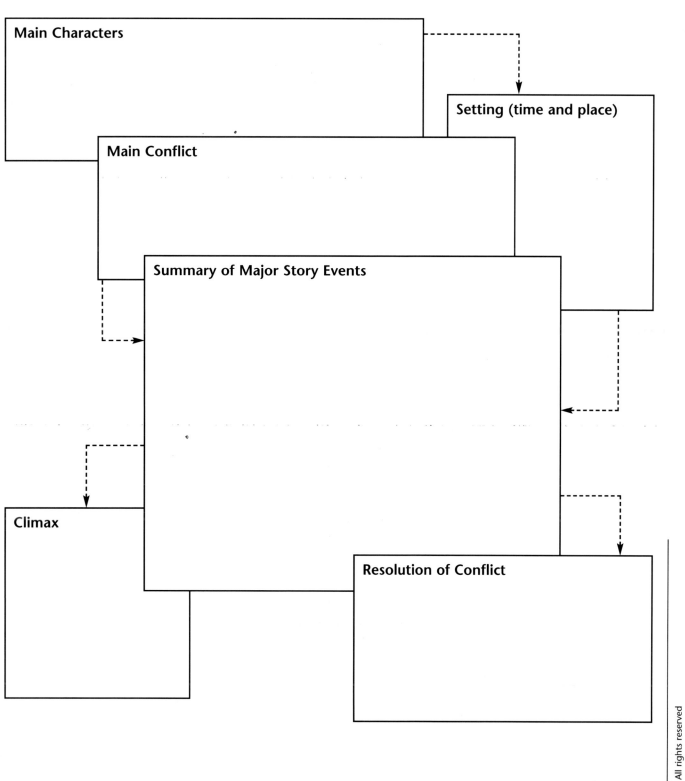

- Main Characters
- Setting (time and place)
- Main Conflict
- Summary of Major Story Events
- Climax
- Resolution of Conflict

Name _____

*(Main Idea and Details)*
**A. True/False:** Mark each with a *T* for true or an *F* for false.

_____ 1. Vladek felt unsettled when Anja insisted on seeing his apartment.

_____ 2. Lucia mocks Anja's appearance.

_____ 3. Anja took pills because she was "so skinny and nervous."

_____ 4. Anja got upset after learning Vladek dated her and Lucia Greenberg simultaneously.

_____ 5. Vladek wants Art to exclude Anja and Lucia from his story because they have nothing to do with the Holocaust.

*(Main Idea and Details)*
**B. Fill in the Blanks**

6. People told _____ that he looked like Rudolph Valentino, who was known as

   "The _____."

7. Vladek dated _____ _____ for three or four years before she suggested they get engaged.

8. The Zylberbergs owned a _____ factory, one of the biggest in

   _____.

9. Anja's father gave Vladek a beautiful _____ _____ as a wedding gift.

10. Vladek gets upset with _____ when she puts Art's jacket on a

    _____ _____.

*(Inferences)*
**C. Open-Ended Comprehension:** On the lines below, explain why Vladek chose to marry Anja instead of Lucia.

_____

_____

_____

_____

_____

Name _____

*(Summarize Major Ideas)*
**A. Short Answer:** Write brief answers to the questions below.

1. Why does Vladek take pills?

   _____

2. What package did Anja give her neighbor?

   _____

3. How did Vladek help Anja while she was at the sanitarium?

   _____

4. What stories had the train passengers heard about Nazis?

   _____

5. What did Vladek see at the riot downtown?

   _____

*(Main Idea and Details)*
**B. True/False:** Mark each with a *T* for true or an *F* for false.

_____ 6. As an older man, Vladek has one eye with a cataract and one glass eye.

_____ 7. Anja helped translate Communist papers for a friend from Warsaw.

_____ 8. Miss Stefanska, Anja's neighbor, told the police about Anja's illegal activities.

_____ 9. Richieu was born premature, and the doctors had to break his arm at birth.

_____ 10. Vladek considered running away after he received his draft notice to join the Polish army.

*(Literary Devices)*
**C. Open-Ended Comprehension:** On the lines below, explain how this chapter foreshadows the treatment Vladek and Anja would experience under Nazi control.

_____

_____

_____

_____

_____

_____

Name _____

*(Main Idea and Details)*
## A. Fill in the Blanks

1. _____ throws away Art's _____ and gives him an old one instead.

2. The Polish officer yelled at Vladek because his gun was _____, and then the Germans scolded him after they discovered his gun was _____.

3. The Germans offered _____ assignments to prisoners in return for abundant _____ and _____.

4. In the prison camp, Vladek _____ in the river and did _____ to stay strong.

5. Vladek waited in a _____ by the river for the Germans to attack.

*(Character Analysis)*
## B. Identification: Match each character with the correct description.

_____ 6. Vladek

_____ 7. Vladek's grandfather

_____ 8. rabbi

_____ 9. Orbach

_____ 10. Vladek's father

a. forced to shave his beard

b. initially avoided the army by starving

c. cared for Vladek after his release from prison camp

d. prophesied Vladek's freedom

e. was afraid he would never leave the prison camp

*(Summarize Major Ideas)*
## C. Open-Ended Comprehension: On the lines below, explain why Vladek finally decided to join the army.

_____

_____

_____

_____

_____

*(Summarize Major Ideas)*
**A. Short Answer:** Write brief answers to the questions below.

1. How did Vladek earn money after he returned from the prison camp?

   _____

2. Why did the elderly members of Anja's family turn themselves in to the Nazis?

   _____

3. Why did Vladek's father climb the fence at *Dienst* Stadium?

   _____

4. Why did people dress in nice clothes to go to the stadium?

   _____

5. How was the tin shop important to Vladek's survival?

   _____


*(Main Idea and Details)*
**B. True/False:** Mark each with a *T* for true or an *F* for false.

_____ 6. Anja's father thought it was too dangerous for Vladek to trade on the black market.

_____ 7. Nazi officers paid half-price for the Zylberbergs' handsome bedroom set.

_____ 8. The Nazis offered sugar as a reward for turning in unregistered Jews.

_____ 9. Vladek sold gold and jewelry because it was easier to hide than clothing.

_____ 10. Anja's family hid her grandparents in the attic so the Nazis could not find them.


*(Summarize Major Ideas)*
**C. Open-Ended Comprehension:** On the lines below, explain the methods Nazis used to separate Jews at *Dienst* Stadium.

_____

_____

_____

_____

_____

_____

Name _____

*(Main Idea and Details)*
**A. True/False:** Mark each with a *T* for true or an *F* for false.

_____ 1. Art's girlfriend Françoise makes him go to Queens to help his father fix the roof.

_____ 2. Art's comic accuses Anja of murder.

_____ 3. Tosha poisoned the children because she thought the Nazis were coming for them.

_____ 4. Haskel could not help Anja's parents due to their age.

_____ 5. Vladek thinks Art is only concerned with inheriting Vladek's money.

*(Main Idea and Details)*
**B. Fill in the Blanks**

6. _____ showed Vladek a secret tunnel made of _____ where they could hide in emergencies.

7. Vladek finds a piece of _____ on the street and keeps it, even though

_____ thinks it is junk.

8. The family builds _____ under the coal bin and in the _____.

9. Persis offers to take the family's _____ to Zawiercie.

10. _____ is upset with Vladek because he has many photos of _____ on his desk.

*(Summarize Major Ideas)*
**C. Open-Ended Comprehension:** On the lines below, describe three methods Vladek and his family used to escape being captured by the Nazis.

_____

_____

_____

_____

_____

_____

_____

© Novel Units, Inc.

Name _____

*(Main Idea and Details)*
## A. Fill in the Blanks

1. Vladek usually rode the streetcar for officials because the _____ paid no attention to him.

2. Anja thought the smuggling plan to get to _____ was too dangerous.

3. Vladek and his friends spoke _____ in front of the smugglers to keep their conversation private.

4. Vladek hid a gold _____ in a can of _____ _____, but the Germans took it away.

5. Art calls his father a _____ because Vladek burned Anja's _____.

*(Summarize Major Ideas)*
## B. Short Answer: Write brief answers to the questions below.

6. How did Vladek convince Anja to go along with the smuggling plan?

   _____

7. How did Vladek respond when Mala asked for new clothes?

   _____

8. What was dangerous about hiding in Mrs. Motonowa's house?

   _____

9. What terrified Anja about hiding in Mrs. Motonowa's cellar?

   _____

10. How were Anja and Vladek finally captured, and where were they taken?

   _____

Name _____

*(Support Responses)*

**C. Open-Ended Comprehension:** On the lines below, explain whether or not you think Art's anger at the end of the book is justified and why.

_____

_____

_____

_____

_____

_____

_____

_____

_____

_____

© Novel Units, Inc.

*(Character Analysis)*
**A. Identification:** Match each character with the correct description.

____ 1. Vladek

____ 2. Persis

____ 3. Anja

____ 4. Art

____ 5. Tosha

____ 6. Mr. Zylberberg

____ 7. Lucia

____ 8. Mala

____ 9. Haskel

____ 10. Mrs. Motonowa

a. thinks her husband is cheap

b. killed herself and several children with poison

c. hid Vladek in her home

d. sent Anja a hurtful letter

e. took pills for her nerves .

f. police officer who worked for the Nazis

g. picks up old wire off the street

h. does not visit his father often

i. accuses his mother of sending him to prison

j. gave Vladek money and credit for his business

**B. Multiple Choice:** Choose the BEST answer.

*(Main Idea and Details)*
____ 11. While visiting the bank, Vladek tells his son that he regrets

(a) getting remarried

(b) being a terrible father

(c) burning Anja's old journals

(d) selling goods on the black market

*(Main Idea and Details)*
____ 12. What did Vladek's Bielsko factory produce?

(a) textiles

(b) ammunition

(c) leather shoes

(d) tin and metals

*(Summarize Major Ideas)*

_____ 13. In her letter to Anja, Lucia claimed that Vladek

(a) was already married

(b) disliked Anja's family

(c) said terrible things about Anja

(d) was dating many other women

*(Main Idea and Details)*

_____ 14. What sight frightened Anja and Vladek on their way to the sanitarium?

(a) fires raging

(b) a Nazi flag waving

(c) Jewish people starving

(d) Polish troops assembling

*(Main Idea and Details)*

_____ 15. How did Vladek's father avoid joining the army?

(a) He left Poland.

(b) He changed his name.

(c) He pulled out his teeth.

(d) He ate until he was overweight.

*(Main Idea and Details)*

_____ 16. What impossible task do the Nazis make Vladek and several other Jewish
prisoners attempt?

(a) cleaning a filthy stable in one hour

(b) burying several dead soldiers in one hour

(c) marching to the prison camp in one hour

(d) shining every Nazi guard's boots in one hour

*(Summarize Major Ideas)*

_____ 17. What happened to the Zylberbergs' valuable bedroom set?

   (a)  The Nazis stole it.

   (d)  The Nazis destroyed it.

   (c)  The Nazis paid half-price for it.

   (d)  The Nazis allowed the family to keep it.

*(Sequencing)*

_____ 18. What do Art and Vladek do after Anja commits suicide?

   (a)  stay with family

   (b)  ignore each other

   (c)  sleep on the floor

   (d)  read Anja's journals

*(Main Idea and Details)*

_____ 19. What animal does the author use to represent Americans?

   (a)  bears

   (b)  cats

   (c)  dogs

   (d)  pigs

*(Compare/Contrast)*

_____ 20. Vladek chose Anja over Lucia because Anja was more

   (a)  attractive

   (b)  fashionable

   (c)  religious

   (d)  sensitive

Name _____

(Main Idea and Details)
## C. Fill in the Blanks

21. Art visits his father in _____ _____ in order to learn about Vladek's past.

22. _____ would not let Vladek go and insisted on being his girlfriend.

23. Vladek throws away Art's _____ without asking.

24. _____ says that Vladek is more attached to _____ than people.

25. Vladek calls Art to help him fix his _____.

26. Art wears a _____ uniform in his comic to represent how he feels about his mother's suicide.

27. Tasha poisons the children to prevent them from going to the _____

    _____.

28. Anja's family builds bunkers in the _____ and in the _____.

29. While in the prison camp, Vladek does _____ to stay in shape and plays

    _____ to keep his mind occupied.

30. The Nazis offer the prisoners abundant _____ and _____ if they

    accept _____ assignments to replace German workers.

(Summarize Major Ideas)
**D. Open-Ended Short Answer:** In one paragraph each, answer the following on a separate sheet of paper.

(a) Explain the effect Anja's suicide had on Art and Vladek.

(b) Explain why Vladek destroyed his wife's journals and why Art thinks Vladek is a murderer.

(c) Explain why Vladek thought hiring the smugglers was a good idea.

(d) Explain what Vladek and Mala think of each other.

(e) Explain why Vladek agreed to perform labor for the Nazis in exchange for leaving the prison camp.

Name _____

**E. Essay:** Complete one of the following in a well-developed essay. Cite specific evidence from the book to support your answer.

*(Theme/Literary Devices)*
(a) Explain how the author uses animals to symbolically represent different religious groups and nationalities. How does this enhance your understanding of the book's theme(s)?

*(Summarize Major Ideas)*
(b) Explain the methods the Nazis used to control, divide, and destroy the Jewish population, and discuss the methods Vladek and his family used to evade the Nazis.

*(Compare/Contrast/Character Analysis)*
(c) Compare and contrast Vladek and Art. Why do you think they have such a strained relationship?

# Answer Key

**Activity #1:** 1. Art Spiegelman 2. Answers will vary. 3. 1973 or 1980–1983 4. 159 5.–6. Answers will vary.

**Activity #2:** Answers will vary.

**Activity #3:** 1. d 2. b 3. c 4. b 5. c 6. b 7. d 8. b; Summaries will vary.

**Activity #4:** Answers will vary. Example: Vocabulary Word: pogrom; Definition—government-sanctioned campaign to kill a certain ethnic group; Synonym—genocide; Antonym—tolerance; Part of Speech—noun; Pronunciation—puh-gruhm; Sentence—The *pogrom* left the city in ruins, and all the homes were reduced to ashes.

**Activity #5:** Answers will vary. Example: Word—rabbi; Explanation—During the Holocaust, rabbis tried to help maintain peace and keep the communities together. Many people turned to rabbis for spiritual support and comfort during this horrific time.

**Activity #6:** Answers will vary. Example: Word—luxurious; Character—Mr. Zylberberg; Explanation—Mr. Zylberberg lived a luxurious life before the Holocaust, yet all of his money could not save him or his family.

**Activity #7:** Crossword puzzles will vary.

**Activity #8:** 1. naïve/pragmatic 2. stereotype/caricature 3. German-inspired/Yiddish 4. center/outskirts 5. forgetful/senile 6. connections/acquaintances; Antonyms—1, 4

## Study Guide

**The Sheik:** 1. Rego Park, New York 2. Mala hangs Art's coat on a wire hanger, and Vladek gets upset that she did not use a wooden one. 3. Lucia was an aggressive woman Art dated who wanted a serious relationship with him. Art's feelings toward Lucia seemed lukewarm in contrast. 4. Although Lucia was more attractive than Anja, Vladek chose Anja because she was sensitive, intelligent, and personable. 5. Anja's parents didn't want her to visit a "bachelor's apartment" because they were "religious and old-fashioned" (p. 18). Instead, Vladek came to Anja's parents' house for dinner the next night. 6. a large, wealthy, conservative family 7. Vladek found pills in Anja's closet. He later discovered that they were just "because she was so skinny and nervous" (p. 19). 8. Anja received a letter in the mail saying terrible things about Vladek, which upset her. Lucia was to blame because she sent the letter out of scorn. 9. Vladek thinks the information about Anja and Lucia is too personal and "has nothing to do with Hitler and the Holocaust" (p. 23).

**The Honeymoon:** 1. Vladek takes pills for his heart and diabetes, as well as over 25 vitamins; Vladek believes he must "fight to save [himself]" (p. 26). 2. Anja translated pamphlets for her Communist friend, which was illegal; When the police came to search their home, Anja hid the documents with Miss Stefanska, a neighbor, who was arrested instead. 3. Vladek wanted to open a textile shop; Anja's father suggested that Vladek open a textile factory instead. 4. Vladek gets distracted from his main story by telling Art how he and his brother Richieu were born. Vladek gestures and knocks over the pills. 5. The family called to inform Vladek that Anja had fallen into a deep depression; Anja immediately went to a sanitarium to recover. 6. They saw a Nazi flag flying in a small town outside Czechoslovakia; They had heard stories about Nazi troops humiliating, beating, and killing Jews. 7. He accompanied her to the sanitarium and "told her many jokes and stories to keep her busy…" [p. 35]. They danced, took walks, and enjoyed each other's company so much that Anja began feeling better about her life. 8. It was robbed. 9. He received a draft notice; Vladek's family immediately left for Sosnowiec.

**Prisoner of War:** 1. Art tells Mala how Vladek used to get angry when Art did not finish all of the food on his plate. Vladek would even save the old food and make Art eat it later. 2. He extracted his own teeth until he had too few to join. He put Vladek and Vladek's older brother on a starvation diet and kept them from sleeping well so the army would deem them too unhealthy to be recruited. 3. The Polish officer scolded Vladek because Vladek's gun was cold, meaning Vladek was not shooting anyone. After the Nazi soldiers captured Vladek, they became angry that his gun was hot, meaning he had fired at them. 4. The Nazis instruct Vladek and several other men to clean a filthy stable in one hour, which was too much work to do in such a short amount of time. 5. Vladek bathed, did gymnastics, prayed, played chess, and wrote letters to stay healthy and strong. 6. The Nazis offered the prisoners jobs as laborers to replace Germans who left to fight in the war effort. Vladek jumped at this opportunity because he wanted "to be treated like a human being" (p. 54) and hoped the job would provide better food and living conditions. 7. Vladek's premonition involved someone who resembled his dead grandfather telling him he would be freed on Parshas Truma. 8. Orbach was a friend of Vladek's uncle, and the Nazis agreed to release Vladek into Orbach's custody. At Orbach's home, Vladek was able to recuperate. 9. German soldiers humiliated Jewish men in the streets by making them cut off their beards. 10. Vladek throws away Art's jacket, which he says is shabby. Art grudgingly accepts his father's gift (Vladek's old jacket) and leaves the house grumbling.

**The Noose Tightens:** 1. Vladek wants to fix the drainpipe on the roof. Art refuses to help Vladek, suggesting he hire someone to fix it instead. 2. Using his old business contacts, Vladek began selling and trading on the black market. 3. The Nazis closed down the street to inspect all Jews' work documentation. Vladek procured forged work documentation from a friend of Anja's father to ensure his safety in the future. 4. The Nazis wanted the Zylberberg's ornate furniture. The family finally agreed to sell it, but when the Nazis came to pick up the furniture, they refused to pay. 5. The Nazis hang Cohn and three others who were "dealing goods without coupons" (p. 83) in order to make examples of them. 6. The Nazis stated that all Jews over 70 years old would be transferred to a facility "better prepared to take care of the elderly" (p. 86); At first the Zylberbergs hid Anja's grandparents, but eventually the Nazis threatened to arrest Anja's parents if her grandparents were not turned in. 7. The Nazis planned to check all Jews' paperwork and separate them accordingly. After members of Vladek's family were sent to the "bad" side of the fence, Vladek's father followed them. 8. Mala accuses Vladek of being "more attached to things than to people" (p. 93). Art brushes off her concern and leaves quickly.

**Mouse Holes:** 1. Mala calls Art for help with Vladek, who is stubbornly insisting he can climb on the roof to fix a leaky drainpipe. Art is annoyed and tries to avoid having to help Mala and his father. 2. Vladek is upset about a comic book Art created years before that tells about Anja's suicide. Art is embarrassed because the comic is very personal, detailing Art's grief and relationship with his father after the incident. 3. Anja came to Art's room late at night and asked if he still loved her. Art turned away from her and said, "Sure, Ma!" 4. Persis, who had influence with the Germans in Zawiercie, offered to take and protect Richieu. The family was hesitant but eventually agreed, and later they found out that Richieu was poisoned by Tosha because she thought Nazis were coming to take her and the children. 5. One was beneath the coal bin in the kitchen of their first house, and the other was in the attic of a different house. They built the bunkers so they would not be apprehended by the Nazis, who were deporting thousands of Jews every week. 6. Vladek's family caught a stranger wandering through their house. Instead of harming him, they took pity on him and released him. He soon informed the Gestapo of their whereabouts. 7. Haskel was Vladek's cousin and "a chief of the Jewish police" (p. 115) who worked with the Nazis. Although he was able to sneak Anja and Vladek out of captivity by pretending they were workers, he was not able to help Anja's parents because they were too old to pass for workers. 8. Vladek collects things that he sees as useful but other people would consider garbage, such as wire. Art thinks his father is cheap and a packrat. He recommends Vladek buy new items instead. 9. Miloch was Haskel's brother who worked in a Nazi shoe repair factory. He showed Vladek a bunker built behind a mountain of shoes. 10. Vladek tells Art that Mala only cares about money. Vladek wishes he had never remarried.

**Mouse Trap:** 1. So far, Vladek is sounding just like "the racist caricature of the miserly old Jew" (p. 131). Art does not want to insult his father, but he wants to portray him accurately. 2. Vladek likes the preliminary drawings and thinks the book will be very successful. He compares Art to Walt Disney. 3. The governess immediately shunned Vladek and Anja. Mr. Lukowski was kinder and allowed the couple to take refuge in the back shed. 4. Mrs. Motonowa was a woman who initially sold Vladek food on the black market. Later, when they needed a place to stay, she allowed the Spiegelmans to live in her home. Mr. Motonowa would turn in the Spiegelmans·if he saw them. 5. Smugglers offered to sneak Vladek and other Jews into Hungary (for a price). To verify that the plan would work, Vladek and the others decided they would send one man to Hungary first to see if he arrived safely. 6. Anja thought the plan was dangerous. After she and Vladek boarded the train, the Gestapo appeared and captured them. One of the smugglers had informed the Germans of the escape attempt before the train left. 7. Vladek helped another prisoner write to his family in German, and the prisoner gratefully shared the food he obtained as a result. 8. Art is angry that Vladek burned his mother's journals, even though Anja wanted Art to read them someday. Art feels that Vladek has "murdered" Anja's memories.

**Note:** Answers to Activities #9–#16 will vary. Suggested responses are given where applicable.

**Activity #9:** Suggestions: In the beginning—Vladek is young and ambitious; Event #1—Vladek finds pills in Anja's closet; Vladek feels concerned; Event #2—Vladek sees the Nazi flag; Vladek feels terrified; Event #3—Vladek returns home from a prison camp; Vladek feels joyful; Event #4—Vladek makes money for his family via the black market; Vladek feels proud; Event #5—Vladek hears that his father went to the "bad side" of *Dienst* Stadium; Vladek feels panicked; Event #6—Vladek finds out about the secret room in the shoe factory; Vladek feels surprised; At the end—Vladek is grateful to be alive.

**Activity #10:** Suggestions: Descriptions—Vladek: thrifty, stubborn; Art: creative, spirited; Mala: harried, incensed; Mr. Zylberberg: noble, wealthy; Anja: unstable, nervous; Relationships—Vladek/Art: tense yet loving; Art/Vladek: exasperating; Vladek/Mala: strained, regretful; Mala/Vladek: frustrating, infuriating; Vladek/Mr. Zylberberg: respectful; Mr. Zylberberg/Vladek: approving, admiring; Vladek/Anja: supportive, protective; Anja/Vladek: dependent, devoted

**Activity #11:** Suggestion for Art: Line 1—Art; Line 2—Lover of comics, creativity, and good stories; Line 3—Giver of advice, affection (on occasion), and false comfort; Line 4—Needs ideas for comics, more contact with his family, and information about Vladek's past; Line 5—Wants to read his mother's journals, to write a memorable story, and to tell the truth about the Holocaust; Line 6—Is good at drawing, writing, and avoiding his father; Line 7—Should work on sympathizing with others, being more social, and controlling his temper; Line 8—Is similar to his father (because he focuses on his own needs above others'), his mother (because he is depressed at certain points in his life), and Mala (because he gets angry at his father simply because of his father's nature); Line 9—Survivor of his mother's suicide, his father's grief, and a tumultuous upbringing; Line 10: Spiegelman

**Activity #12:** Example: Problem—Vladek calls early in the morning requesting that Art help him fix a leaky drainpipe; Character's Solution—Art avoids helping his father until Vladek finds a neighbor that will help him; Your Solution—Answers will vary, but perhaps Art could have offered to help his father later in the day.

**Activity #13:** 1. The last one to the schoolyard is the slowest or least motivated to win. 2. Doctors only give Vladek prescriptions for drugs he deems useless. 3. Art and Mala both think money is abundant and are prone to spend freely. 4. German-organized events ran like clockwork. 5. That coffee is as old as an oak tree!

**Activity #14:** Answers will vary.

**Activity #15:** Suggestions: Pros—Vladek will not suffer the painful Holocaust memories the journals induced; Vladek will be more able to "let Anja go" if this physical reminder of her presence is gone; Cons—Art will not be able to use his mother's personal accounts for his book; Vladek has destroyed a valuable historical record; Art has lost a vital connection to his mother.

**Activity #16:** Main Characters—Vladek, Anja, Art, Mala; Setting—Holocaust-era Poland and modern-day Rego Park, New York; Main Conflict—Art needs subject matter for his new project, but his strained relationship with his father makes their interviews difficult; Summary of Major Story Events— Vladek begins telling Art about his life before and during World War II. Vladek met and married Anja before the Holocaust began. The two endured the escalation of the Nazi threat in Poland. They hid and were apprehended several times. They lost their first son, Richieu, but managed to survive through the end of the conflict. Anja killed herself years later, and now Vladek lives in Rego Park, New York with his second wife, Mala. Climax—Though the story has many, a climax occurs when Vladek and Anja are apprehended on the train to Hungary; Resolution of Conflict—The father/son conflict is not really resolved, as Art storms off after learning Vladek burned all of Anja's old journals. However, the reader can glean from Art's actions and words that he accepts his father, flaws and all, at the end of the book.

**Quiz #1: A.** 1. F 2. T 3. T (p. 19) 4. F 5. T **B.** 6. Vladek/Sheik 7. Lucia Greenberg 8. hosiery/Poland 9. gold watch 10. Mala/wire hanger **C.** Answers will vary. Refer to the scoring rubric on page 39 of this guide.

**Quiz #2: A.** 1. Vladek takes pills for his heart, diabetes, and basic health. 2. Anja gave her neighbor a package of Communist literature that the police were searching for. 3. Vladek made jokes, told stories, and danced with Anja. 4. The passengers heard that Nazis took away Jewish businesses and mocked and humiliated Jews in the streets. 5. He saw a large crowd yelling "Jews out! Jews out!" (p. 37) and two people being killed while the police just watched. **B.** 6. T 7. T 8. F 9. F 10. F **C.** Answers will vary. Refer to the scoring rubric on page 39 of this guide.

**Quiz #3: A.** 1. Vladek/jacket 2. cold/hot 3. labor/housing/food 4. bathed/gymnastics 5. trench **B.** 6. b 7. d 8. e 9. c 10. a **C.** Answers will vary. Refer to the scoring rubric on page 39 of this guide.

**Quiz #4: A.** 1. Vladek made deals with shops that still owed him money and traded the goods on the black market. 2. The Nazis threatened to take Anja's parents in place of the grandparents. 3. His daughter and grandchildren were sent to the "bad side" of the fence, and he did not want them to be alone. 4. Everyone wanted to appear young and able-bodied so they would get a good stamp on their passport. 5. Vladek was able to obtain a priority work card there, and it was also a place he could hide during a round-up. **B.** 6. F 7. F 8. T 9. T 10. F **C.** Answers will vary. Refer to the scoring rubric on page 39 of this guide.

**Quiz #5: A.** 1. F 2. T 3. T 4. T 5. F **B.** 6. Miloch/shoes 7. wire/Art 8. bunkers/attic 9. children 10. Mala/Anja **C.** Answers will vary. Refer to the scoring rubric on page 39 of this guide.

**Quiz #6: A.** 1. Germans 2. Hungary 3. Yiddish 4. watch/shoe polish 5. murderer/journals OR diaries **B.** 6. Vladek showed Anja the letter from Abraham, who arrived safely in Hungary. 7. He offered her Anja's old clothes. 8. Her husband came home sometimes, and he would have turned them in. Also, Mrs. Motonowa sold goods on the black market and could have been caught doing this at any time. 9. There were giant rats living in the cellar. 10. Anja and Vladek were captured by Nazis on the train bound for Hungary because one of the smugglers was an informant. They were initially sent to a regular prison but were later sent to Auschwitz. **C.** Answers will vary. Refer to the scoring rubric on page 39 of this guide.

**Final Test: A.** 1. g 2. h 3. e 4. i 5. b 6. j 7. d 8. a 9. f 10. c **B.** 11. a 12. a 13. d 14. b 15. c 16. a 17. a 18. c 19. c 20. d **C.** 21. Rego Park 22. Lucia 23. jacket 24. Mala/things 25. roof OR drainpipe 26. prison 27. gas chambers 28. cellar/attic 29. gymnastics/chess 30. housing/food/labor **D.–E.** Responses will vary. Refer to the scoring rubric on page 39 of this guide.

# Linking Novel Units® Student Packets to National and State Reading Assessments

During the past several years, an increasing number of students have faced some form of state-mandated competency testing in reading. Many states now administer state-developed assessments to measure the skills and knowledge emphasized in their particular reading curriculum. This Novel Units® guide includes open-ended comprehension questions that correlate with state-mandated reading assessments. The rubric below provides important information for evaluating responses to open-ended comprehension questions. Teachers may also use scoring rubrics provided for their own state's competency test.

## Scoring Rubric for Open-Ended Items

**3-Exemplary**
Thorough, complete ideas/information
Clear organization throughout
Logical reasoning/conclusions
Thorough understanding of reading task
Accurate, complete response

**2-Sufficient**
Many relevant ideas/pieces of information
Clear organization throughout most of response
Minor problems in logical reasoning/conclusions
General understanding of reading task
Generally accurate and complete response

**1-Partially Sufficient**
Minimally relevant ideas/information
Obvious gaps in organization
Obvious problems in logical reasoning/conclusions
Minimal understanding of reading task
Inaccuracies/incomplete response

**0-Insufficient**
Irrelevant ideas/information
No coherent organization
Major problems in logical reasoning/conclusions
Little or no understanding of reading task
Generally inaccurate/incomplete response

# Notes